Math·A·Draw

Level III · Subtraction

27 dot-to-dot math learning games
sequenced according to level of difficulty

Judith N. Parsons

Fearon Teacher Aids
Torrance, California
A Division of Frank Schaffer Publications, Inc.

ISBN—0—8224—4571—9

Printed in the United States of America.
1.9 8 7 6 5 4 3

Contents

Subtraction from zero with checking. Zero in one's and ten's places.   Sets **24** and **25**

Subtraction from zero with checking. Zero in one's, ten's, and hundred's places.   Sets **26** and **27**

Answer Key

Introduction

Math-A-Draw III has been thoroughly classroom tested and used with success to supplement math texts for students in high second, third, and low fourth grade. Most teachers find that students need considerably more practice with basic math skills than is provided in the standard texts. Math-A-Draw materials are designed to provide both this practice and the all-important motivation for students to "stick with it" until they have mastered the skill involved. Most teachers will agree that it's easy to provide problems for practice but much harder to provide effective motivation. Math-A-Draw meets this critical need in several ways.

Math-A-Draw III contains 27 problem sets. Each set includes an A and a B worksheet. The A worksheet provides basic subtraction problems to be solved by your students. The B worksheet provides a dot-to-dot activity containing a hidden picture.

Your students will work and solve the problems on worksheet A and then use their answers, in order, to connect the dots on worksheet B. As they connect the dots, the hidden picture emerges to surprise and delight them. An answer key is provided in the back of the book so that you may check students' work easily or so that the students may check their own answers.

A record card is provided so that you can monitor each student's progress through the Math-A-Draw sequence. A certificate of congratulations is also included. This may be awarded to each student as he or she successfully completes the Math-A-Draw III series.

Math-A-Draw III materials are ideal companions to high second, third, or low fourth grade math texts. For example, after subtraction from 10 with regrouping has been taught, the corresponding Math-A-Draw III activities will provide highly motivating practice. Problem sets are carefully sequenced to provide practice reinforcement for each step in learning math concepts and skills.

For students, connecting the dots to find the hidden picture and coloring the completed drawings provide an incentive to solve the problems correctly and move on to new material. Solving an arithmetic problem and then using the answer to create a picture reinforces many additional skills: identifying numbers, following directions, understanding spatial relationships, sequencing, and so Literally having something to show for their work ensures students a high level of motivation and imparts a sense of closure.

How to Use Math-A-Draw as a Class Activity

Follow these steps to introduce Math-A-Draw to your class:

1. Reproduce the A and B worksheets for Set 1 for each student. Be sure to reproduce extra B worksheets, as some students like to start over if they make a mistake.

2. Pass out the A worksheets. Keep the B worksheets at your desk. (When the B worksheets are passed out with the A worksheets, students may try to guess at the picture and then use the numbers from worksheet B as answers to worksheet A's problems.)

3. Have the students work all the problems on worksheet A. Ask them to work rapidly but carefully. Explain that they will need to have all the answers right in order to find the hidden picture, which you will pass out in a few minutes.

4. Check the answers. It is important that answers be checked as soon as possible after the student has finished solving the problems so that excitement about doing worksheet B does not dissipate. You, the student, or another student may check the answers. If a student has done more than two problems incorrectly, have him or her try to solve those problems again. Be sure that each student has all the answers on worksheet A right, even if you do not have her or him redo any problems. Do not pass out worksheet B until you are sure that all problems have been checked and the correct answers have been written on worksheet A.

5. Pass out worksheet B. In subsequent lessons, worksheet B may be given to individual students as soon as they complete worksheet A and their answers have been checked. Seeing another student trying to find the hidden picture is often a strong incentive for a student to finish his or her worksheet.

6. Be sure that all students have both the completed and checked worksheet A and worksheet B directly in front of them.

7. Say, "Look at worksheet B. Put your pencil on the dot with the arrow. This is where you will start every time you do a Math-A-Draw picture. Notice that the number next to the dot with the arrow is the same as the answer to problem 1A on worksheet A. Now look at the answer to problem 1B. Put your finger just below this answer. Now look at worksheet B and find the dot with the same number next to it. Draw a line from the dot with the arrow to this dot. Now look at worksheet A again. Find the answer to problem 1C. Find the dot on worksheet B with that number. Draw a line from the second dot to this one. Do the rest of the dot-to-dot picture in the same way. Every dot on worksheet B has a number, and each number matches an answer on worksheet A. Be sure to read the answers on worksheet A in order. If you have any trouble, raise your hand, and I'll come help you."

8. Pass out crayons or colored pencils and let students color their completed drawings.

Useful Tips

1. Here's an effective way to explain Math-A-Draw to your students:

   a. Copy the problems in Figure 1 on the left side of the chalkboard.
   b. Copy the incomplete dot-to-dot drawing (Figure 2) on the right side of the board.
   c. Solve the math problems with your students.
   d. Show the students how to use the math answers to connect the dots in proper sequence, and complete the drawing (Figure 3).

2. Make copies of the Math-A-Draw record card to keep track of student progress. Make a record card for each student in your class. You will probably find it easiest to keep the record cards

Figure 1

A	B	C	D	E	F

1

$$10 - 3 = 7 \quad\nearrow\searrow\quad 7 + 3 = 10$$
$$20 - 11 = 9 \quad\nearrow\searrow\quad 9 + 11 = 20$$
$$12 - 8 = 4 \quad\nearrow\searrow\quad 4 + 8 = 12$$

2

$$15 - 12 = 3 \quad\nearrow\searrow\quad 3 + 12 = 15$$
$$11 - 5 = 6 \quad\nearrow\searrow\quad 6 + 5 = 11$$

Figure 2   Figure 3

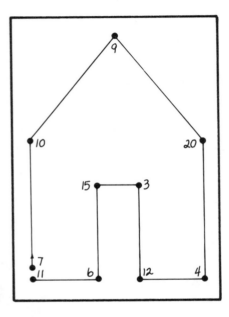

in your desk, as some students tend to lose them when they have to keep them over a period of weeks. However, you may wish to give the students envelopes and ask them to keep the record cards in their own desks or in a central file. As students finish the Math-A-Draw exercises, you may wish to indicate progress by using a hole punch to punch a hole by the completed set number (students love to do this themselves) or by marking the appropriate circle with a crayon or colored pen to indicate how well the student has done. For example, for excellent work, color the circle red; for satisfactory work, green; for unsatisfactory work, blue. After the students have completed all the Math-A-Draw sets, award copies of the Math-A-Draw Certificate to those whose work has been satisfactory to excellent.

THIS IS

_____

MATH•A•DRAW RECORD.

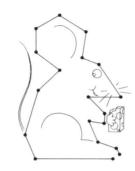

1	2	3
4	5	6
7	8	9
10	11	12
13	14	15
16	17	18
19	20	21
22	23	24
25	26	27

Congratulations

_____

**for excellence in
MATH•A•DRAW**

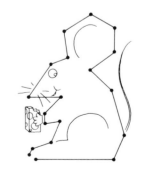

_____
TEACHER

_____
DATE

Name _____

Answer each subtraction problem.
Then, check it by addition.

A   B   C   D   E   F

1
$$70 \quad 66$$
$$-\ 4 \quad +\ 4$$
$$66 \quad 70$$

$$20$$
$$-\ 12 \quad +\ 12$$
$$20$$

$$40$$
$$-\ 29 \quad +\ 29$$
$$40$$

2
$$60$$
$$-\ 39 \quad +\ 39$$

$$30$$
$$-\ 18 \quad +\ 18$$

$$80$$
$$-\ 43 \quad +\ 43$$

3
$$50$$
$$-\ 33 \quad +\ 33$$

$$90$$
$$-\ 89 \quad +\ 89$$

$$10$$
$$-\ 7 \quad +\ 7$$

4
$$350$$
$$-\ 35 \quad +\ 35$$

$$270$$
$$-\ 62 \quad +\ 62$$

$$190$$
$$-\ 87 \quad +\ 87$$

5
$$250$$
$$-\ 9 \quad +\ 9$$

$$380$$
$$-\ 58 \quad +\ 58$$

$$260$$
$$-\ 43 \quad +\ 43$$

6
$$150$$
$$-\ 40 \quad +\ 40$$

$$450$$
$$-\ 204 \quad +\ 204$$

$$390$$
$$-\ 127 \quad +\ 127$$

Name _____

To find the hidden picture, draw lines from dot to dot. Follow
the order of your answers. Start from the dot with the arrow.

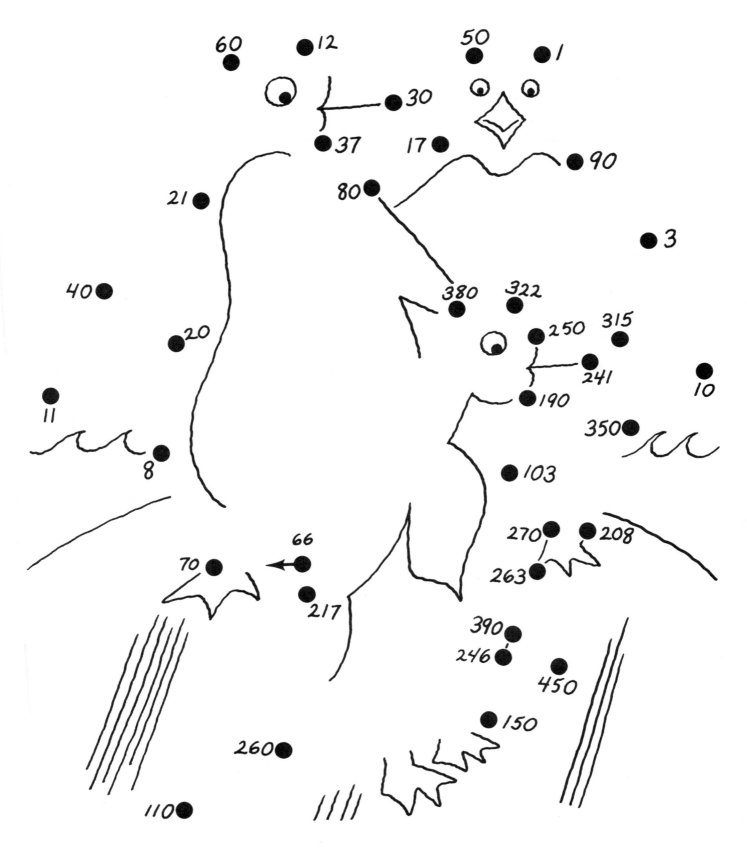

Name _____

Answer each subtraction problem.
Then, check it by addition.

	A	B	C	D	E	F

1

$$\begin{array}{r}180\\-73\\\hline\end{array}$$ $$\begin{array}{r}+73\\\hline 180\end{array}$$

$$\begin{array}{r}780\\-577\\\hline\end{array}$$ $$\begin{array}{r}+577\\\hline 780\end{array}$$

$$\begin{array}{r}580\\-268\\\hline\end{array}$$ $$\begin{array}{r}+268\\\hline\end{array}$$

2

$$\begin{array}{r}450\\-230\\\hline\end{array}$$ $$\begin{array}{r}+230\\\hline\end{array}$$

$$\begin{array}{r}770\\-658\\\hline\end{array}$$ $$\begin{array}{r}+658\\\hline\end{array}$$

$$\begin{array}{r}320\\-13\\\hline\end{array}$$ $$\begin{array}{r}+13\\\hline\end{array}$$

3

$$\begin{array}{r}690\\-68\\\hline\end{array}$$ $$\begin{array}{r}+68\\\hline\end{array}$$

$$\begin{array}{r}990\\-36\\\hline\end{array}$$ $$\begin{array}{r}+36\\\hline\end{array}$$

$$\begin{array}{r}840\\-420\\\hline\end{array}$$ $$\begin{array}{r}+420\\\hline\end{array}$$

4

$$\begin{array}{r}640\\-339\\\hline\end{array}$$ $$\begin{array}{r}+339\\\hline\end{array}$$

$$\begin{array}{r}670\\-447\\\hline\end{array}$$ $$\begin{array}{r}+447\\\hline\end{array}$$

$$\begin{array}{r}340\\-23\\\hline\end{array}$$ $$\begin{array}{r}+23\\\hline\end{array}$$

5

$$\begin{array}{r}160\\-45\\\hline\end{array}$$ $$\begin{array}{r}+45\\\hline\end{array}$$

$$\begin{array}{r}930\\-420\\\hline\end{array}$$ $$\begin{array}{r}+420\\\hline\end{array}$$

$$\begin{array}{r}480\\-327\\\hline\end{array}$$ $$\begin{array}{r}+327\\\hline\end{array}$$

6

$$\begin{array}{r}350\\-223\\\hline\end{array}$$ $$\begin{array}{r}+223\\\hline\end{array}$$

$$\begin{array}{r}720\\-18\\\hline\end{array}$$ $$\begin{array}{r}+18\\\hline\end{array}$$

$$\begin{array}{r}390\\-266\\\hline\end{array}$$ $$\begin{array}{r}+\\\hline\end{array}$$

To find the hidden picture, draw lines from dot to dot. Follow
the order of your answers. Start from the dot with the arrow.

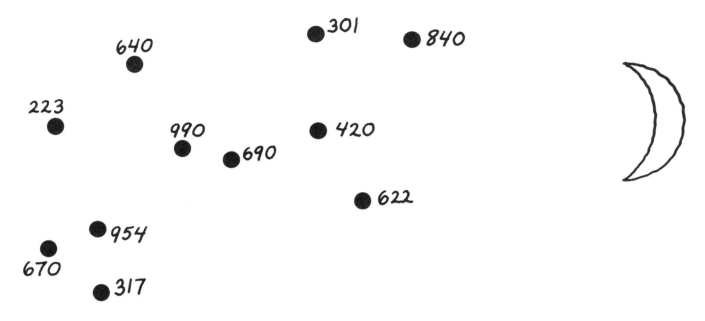

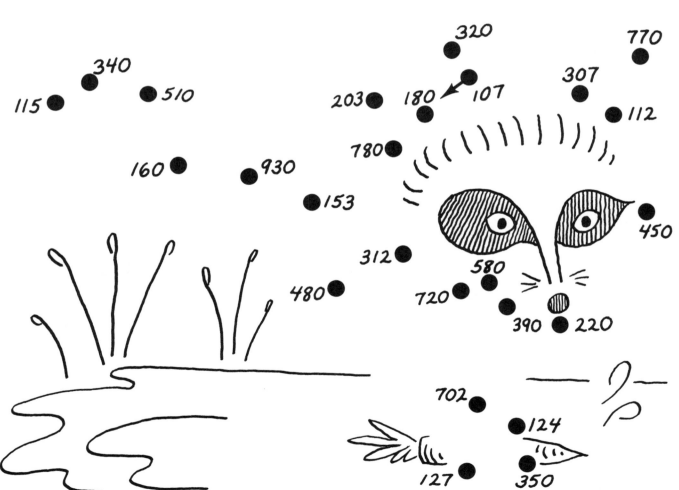

Name _____

Answer each subtraction problem.
Then, check it by addition.

	A	B	C	D	E	F

1.
$$\begin{array}{r} 300 \\ -\ 80 \end{array} \qquad \begin{array}{r} +\ 80 \end{array}$$

$$\begin{array}{r} 800 \\ -790 \end{array} \qquad \begin{array}{r} + \end{array}$$

$$\begin{array}{r} 806 \\ -365 \end{array} \qquad \begin{array}{r} +365 \end{array}$$

2.
$$\begin{array}{r} 920 \\ -815 \end{array} \qquad \begin{array}{r} +815 \end{array}$$

$$\begin{array}{r} 720 \\ -520 \end{array} \qquad \begin{array}{r} +520 \end{array}$$

$$\begin{array}{r} 660 \\ -\ 59 \end{array} \qquad \begin{array}{r} +\ 59 \end{array}$$

3.
$$\begin{array}{r} 808 \\ -755 \end{array} \qquad \begin{array}{r} +755 \end{array}$$

$$\begin{array}{r} 640 \\ -\ 27 \end{array} \qquad \begin{array}{r} +\ 27 \end{array}$$

$$\begin{array}{r} 509 \\ -378 \end{array} \qquad \begin{array}{r} +378 \end{array}$$

4.
$$\begin{array}{r} 707 \\ -463 \end{array} \qquad \begin{array}{r} +463 \end{array}$$

$$\begin{array}{r} 807 \\ -222 \end{array} \qquad \begin{array}{r} +222 \end{array}$$

$$\begin{array}{r} 409 \\ -\ 76 \end{array} \qquad \begin{array}{r} +\ 76 \end{array}$$

5.
$$\begin{array}{r} 530 \\ -324 \end{array} \qquad \begin{array}{r} +324 \end{array}$$

$$\begin{array}{r} 307 \\ -193 \end{array} \qquad \begin{array}{r} +193 \end{array}$$

$$\begin{array}{r} 490 \\ -349 \end{array} \qquad \begin{array}{r} +349 \end{array}$$

6.
$$\begin{array}{r} 709 \\ -\ 93 \end{array} \qquad \begin{array}{r} +\ 93 \end{array}$$

$$\begin{array}{r} 540 \\ -\ 26 \end{array} \qquad \begin{array}{r} + \end{array}$$

$$\begin{array}{r} 990 \\ -250 \end{array} \qquad \begin{array}{r} +250 \end{array}$$

Name _____ Set **3** Worksheet **B**

To find the hidden picture, draw lines from dot to dot. Follow
the order of your answers. Start from the dot with the arrow.

Name _____

Answer each subtraction problem.
Then, check it by addition.

	A	B	C	D	E	F

1.
```
  51        + 3      81        + 6      61        + 60
-  3               -  6               - 60
```

2.
```
  71    + 66     91    + 56     31    + 21
- 66             - 56           - 21
```

3.
```
  41    + 16     221    + 15     181    + 30
- 16             - 15            - 30
```

4.
```
 691    + 65     391    +  8     571    + 24
-  65            -   8           - 24
```

5.
```
 341    + 25     321    + 15     191    + 85
-  25            - 15            - 85
```

6.
```
 681    +  4     351    + 40     781    + 36
-   4            - 40            - 36
```

Name _____   Set **4** Worksheet **B**

To find the hidden picture, draw lines from dot to dot. Follow
the order of your answers. Start from the dot with the arrow.

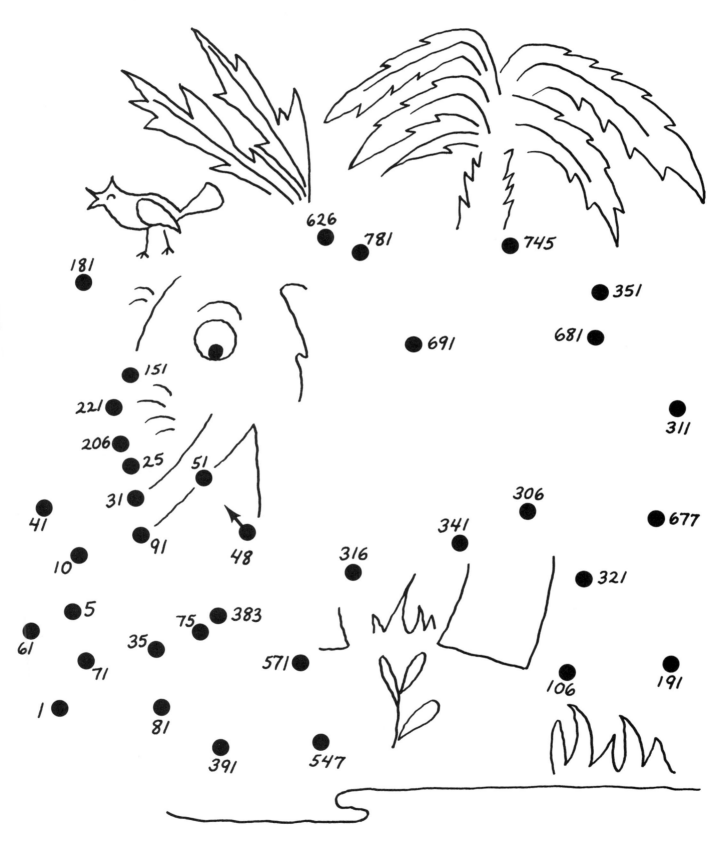

Name _____

Answer each subtraction problem.
Then, check it by addition.

	A	B	C	D	E	F

1
$$\begin{array}{r} 991 \\ -\ 49 \\ \hline \end{array}$$
$+\ 49$
$$\begin{array}{r} 761 \\ -\ 33 \\ \hline \end{array}$$
$+\ 33$
$$\begin{array}{r} 971 \\ -834 \\ \hline \end{array}$$
$+834$

2
$$\begin{array}{r} 941 \\ -326 \\ \hline \end{array}$$
$+326$
$$\begin{array}{r} 361 \\ -155 \\ \hline \end{array}$$
$+155$
$$\begin{array}{r} 751 \\ -335 \\ \hline \end{array}$$
$+335$

3
$$\begin{array}{r} 821 \\ -805 \\ \hline \end{array}$$
$+$ _____
$$\begin{array}{r} 961 \\ -\ 53 \\ \hline \end{array}$$
$+$ _____
$$\begin{array}{r} 861 \\ -532 \\ \hline \end{array}$$
$+$ _____

4
$$\begin{array}{r} 871 \\ -555 \\ \hline \end{array}$$
$+$ _____
$$\begin{array}{r} 851 \\ -\ 4 \\ \hline \end{array}$$
$+$ _____
$$\begin{array}{r} 571 \\ -356 \\ \hline \end{array}$$
$+$ _____

5
$$\begin{array}{r} 651 \\ -430 \\ \hline \end{array}$$
$+$ _____
$$\begin{array}{r} 891 \\ -465 \\ \hline \end{array}$$
$+$ _____
$$\begin{array}{r} 741 \\ -\ 8 \\ \hline \end{array}$$
$+$ _____

6
$$\begin{array}{r} 841 \\ -712 \\ \hline \end{array}$$
$+$ _____
$$\begin{array}{r} 946 \\ -321 \\ \hline \end{array}$$
$+$ _____
$$\begin{array}{r} 771 \\ -765 \\ \hline \end{array}$$
$+$ _____

Math-A-Draw III Copyright © 1984

Name _____ Set **5** Worksheet **B**

To find the hidden picture, draw lines from dot to dot. Follow
the order of your answers. Start from the dot with the arrow.

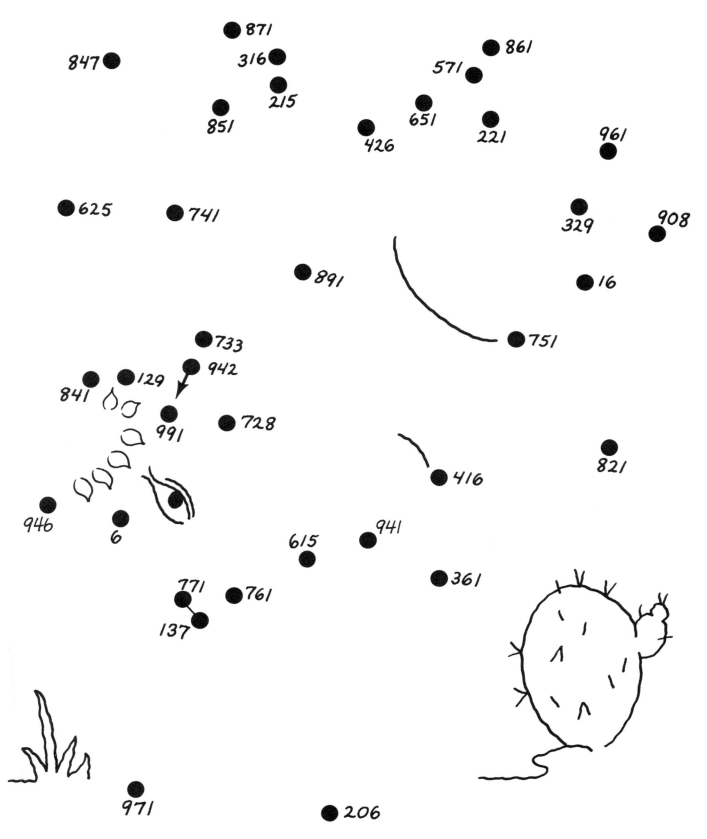

Answer each subtraction problem.
Then, check it by addition.

	A	B	C	D	E	F
1	814 − 82	+ 82	915 − 322	+ 322	121 − 18	+ 18
2	951 − 439	+ 439	919 − 368	+ 368	816 − 423	+ 423
3	881 − 28	+	918 − 97	+	431 − 407	+
4	413 − 333	+	841 − 227	+	941 − 538	+
5	917 − 57	+	791 − 76	+	491 − 255	+
6	751 − 329	+	831 − 408	+	615 − 244	+

To find the hidden picture, draw lines from dot to dot. Follow the order of your answers. Start from the dot with the arrow.

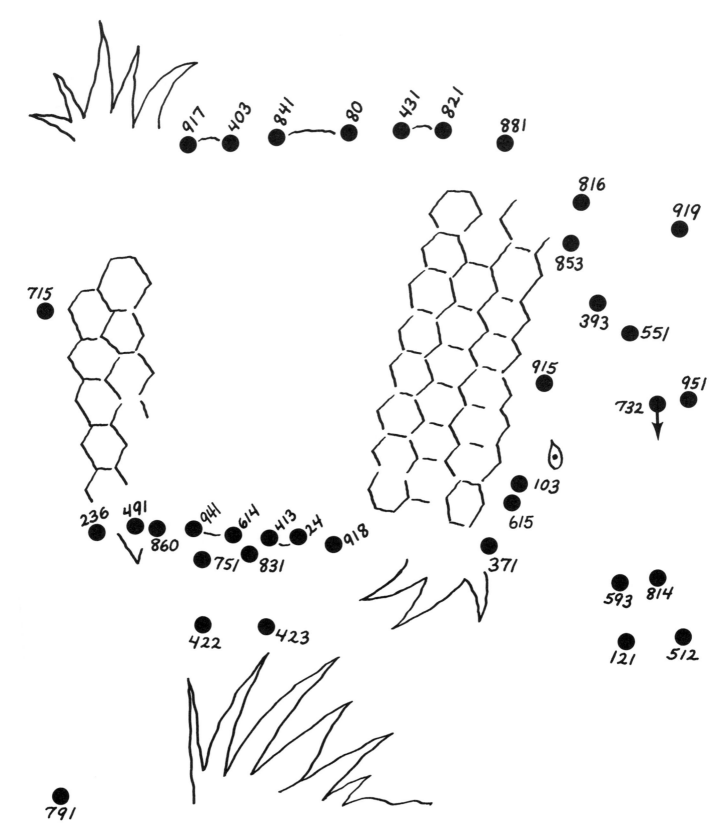

Name _____

Answer each subtraction problem.
Then, check it by addition.

	A	B	C	D	E	F

1

$$
\begin{array}{r} 813 \\ -263 \\ \hline \end{array}
\qquad
\begin{array}{r} \\ +263 \\ \hline \end{array}
\qquad
\begin{array}{r} 410 \\ -106 \\ \hline \end{array}
\qquad
\begin{array}{r} \\ +106 \\ \hline \end{array}
\qquad
\begin{array}{r} 819 \\ -493 \\ \hline \end{array}
\qquad
\begin{array}{r} \\ +493 \\ \hline \end{array}
$$

2

$$
\begin{array}{r} 708 \\ -444 \\ \hline \end{array}
\qquad
\begin{array}{r} \\ +444 \\ \hline \end{array}
\qquad
\begin{array}{r} 690 \\ -587 \\ \hline \end{array}
\qquad
\begin{array}{r} \\ +587 \\ \hline \end{array}
\qquad
\begin{array}{r} 408 \\ -\ 36 \\ \hline \end{array}
\qquad
\begin{array}{r} \\ +\ 36 \\ \hline \end{array}
$$

3

$$
\begin{array}{r} 911 \\ -602 \\ \hline \end{array}
\qquad +\ \underline{\quad}
\qquad
\begin{array}{r} 806 \\ -533 \\ \hline \end{array}
\qquad +\ \underline{\quad}
\qquad
\begin{array}{r} 891 \\ -780 \\ \hline \end{array}
\qquad +\ \underline{\quad}
$$

4

$$
\begin{array}{r} 905 \\ -\ 71 \\ \hline \end{array}
\qquad +\ \underline{\quad}
\qquad
\begin{array}{r} 580 \\ -324 \\ \hline \end{array}
\qquad +\ \underline{\quad}
\qquad
\begin{array}{r} 913 \\ -803 \\ \hline \end{array}
\qquad +\ \underline{\quad}
$$

5

$$
\begin{array}{r} 341 \\ -227 \\ \hline \end{array}
\qquad +\ \underline{\quad}
\qquad
\begin{array}{r} 431 \\ -\ 17 \\ \hline \end{array}
\qquad +\ \underline{\quad}
\qquad
\begin{array}{r} 816 \\ -\ 95 \\ \hline \end{array}
\qquad +\ \underline{\quad}
$$

6

$$
\begin{array}{r} 709 \\ -\ 86 \\ \hline \end{array}
\qquad +\ \underline{\quad}
\qquad
\begin{array}{r} 999 \\ -645 \\ \hline \end{array}
\qquad +\ \underline{\quad}
\qquad
\begin{array}{r} 718 \\ -\ 96 \\ \hline \end{array}
\qquad +\ \underline{\quad}
$$

To find the hidden picture, draw lines from dot to dot. Follow the order of your answers. Start from the dot with the arrow.

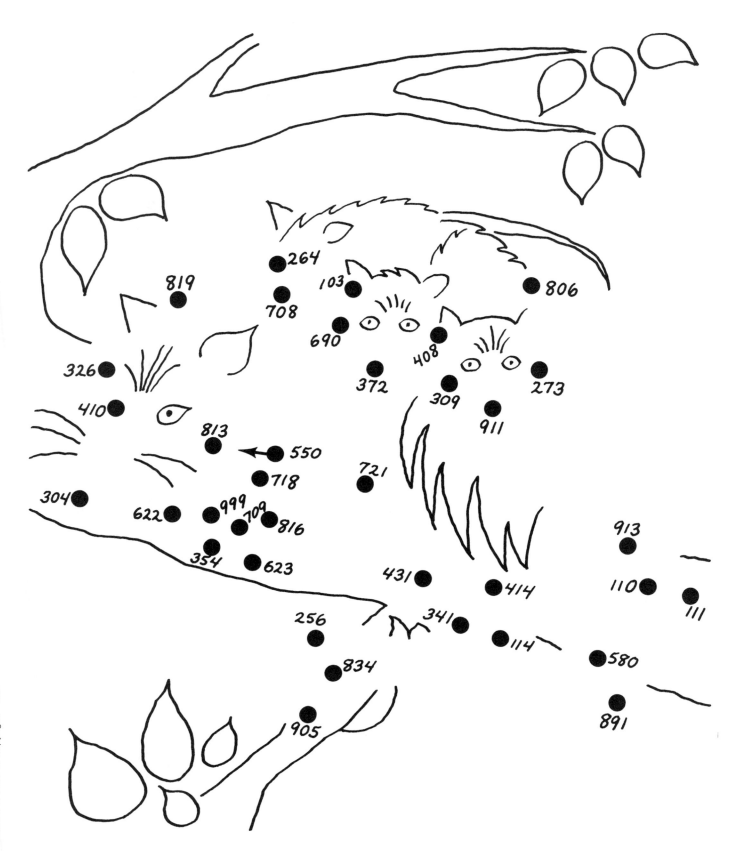

Name _____

Answer each subtraction problem.
Then, check it by addition.

	A	B	C	D	E	F
1	42 − 7	+ 7	32 − 9	+ 9	342 − 29	+ 29
2	725 − 82	+	821 − 90	+	723 − 81	+
3	462 − 29	+	832 − 29	+	322 − 15	+
4	522 − 10	+	629 − 94	+	742 − 18	+
5	128 − 56	+	526 − 35	+	425 − 91	+
6	982 − 347	+	529 − 347	+	329 − 248	+

To find the hidden picture, draw lines from dot to dot. Follow the order of your answers. Start from the dot with the arrow.

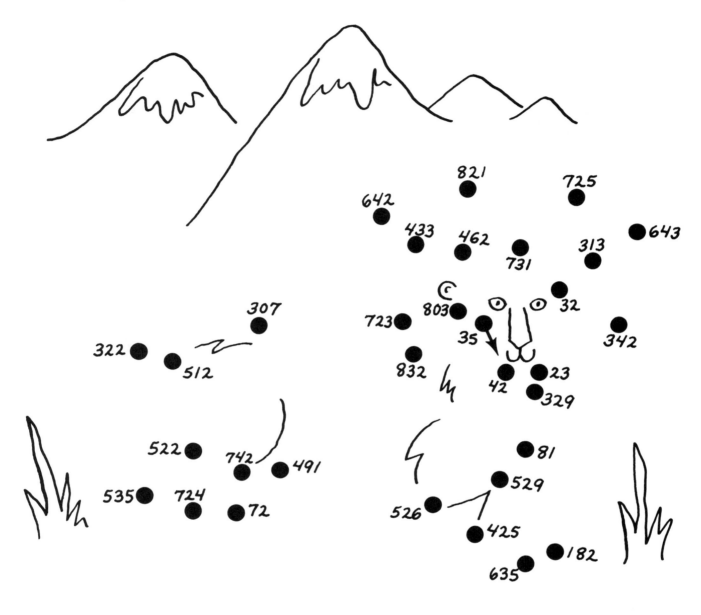

Name _____ Set **9** Worksheet **A**

Answer each subtraction problem.
Then, check it by addition.

	A	B	C	D	E	F

1
$$
\begin{array}{r}922\\-805\\\hline\end{array}
\quad
\begin{array}{r}+805\\\hline\end{array}
\qquad
\begin{array}{r}429\\-375\\\hline\end{array}
\quad
\begin{array}{r}+375\\\hline\end{array}
\qquad
\begin{array}{r}852\\-729\\\hline\end{array}
\quad
\begin{array}{r}+729\\\hline\end{array}
$$

2
$$
\begin{array}{r}782\\-566\\\hline\end{array}
\quad
\begin{array}{r}+\\\hline\end{array}
\qquad
\begin{array}{r}526\\-384\\\hline\end{array}
\quad
\begin{array}{r}+\\\hline\end{array}
\qquad
\begin{array}{r}827\\-516\\\hline\end{array}
\quad
\begin{array}{r}+\\\hline\end{array}
$$

3
$$
\begin{array}{r}629\\-568\\\hline\end{array}
\quad
\begin{array}{r}+\\\hline\end{array}
\qquad
\begin{array}{r}927\\-645\\\hline\end{array}
\quad
\begin{array}{r}+\\\hline\end{array}
\qquad
\begin{array}{r}726\\-594\\\hline\end{array}
\quad
\begin{array}{r}+\\\hline\end{array}
$$

4
$$
\begin{array}{r}829\\-758\\\hline\end{array}
\quad
\begin{array}{r}+\\\hline\end{array}
\qquad
\begin{array}{r}322\\-206\\\hline\end{array}
\quad
\begin{array}{r}+\\\hline\end{array}
\qquad
\begin{array}{r}722\\-\ 10\\\hline\end{array}
\quad
\begin{array}{r}+\\\hline\end{array}
$$

5
$$
\begin{array}{r}622\\-\ 91\\\hline\end{array}
\quad
\begin{array}{r}+\\\hline\end{array}
\qquad
\begin{array}{r}822\\-509\\\hline\end{array}
\quad
\begin{array}{r}+\\\hline\end{array}
\qquad
\begin{array}{r}427\\-\ 95\\\hline\end{array}
\quad
\begin{array}{r}+\\\hline\end{array}
$$

6
$$
\begin{array}{r}821\\-560\\\hline\end{array}
\quad
\begin{array}{r}+\\\hline\end{array}
\qquad
\begin{array}{r}326\\-\ 42\\\hline\end{array}
\quad
\begin{array}{r}+\\\hline\end{array}
\qquad
\begin{array}{r}825\\-793\\\hline\end{array}
\quad
\begin{array}{r}+\\\hline\end{array}
$$

To find the hidden picture, draw lines from dot to dot. Follow
the order of your answers. Start from the dot with the arrow.

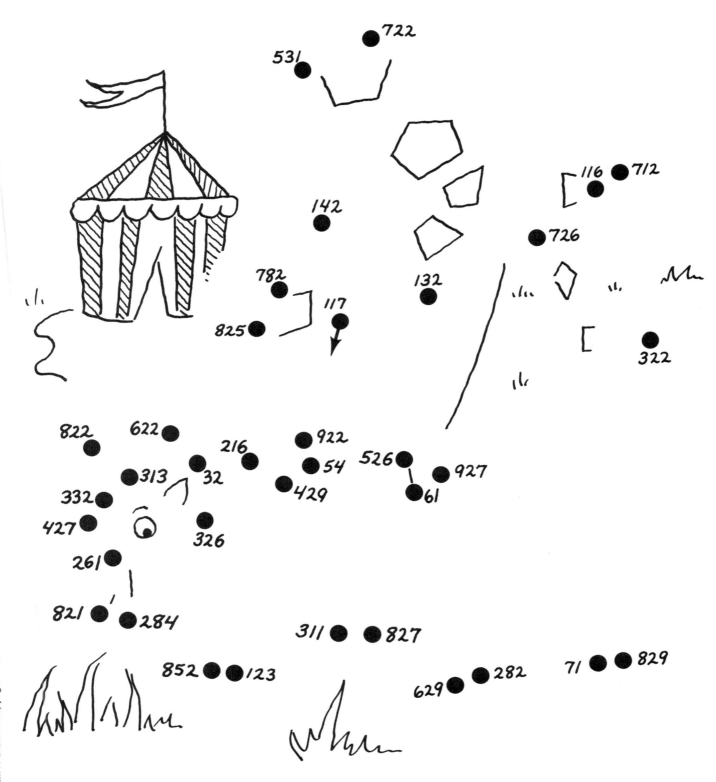

Name _____

Answer each subtraction problem.
Then, check it by addition.

	A	B	C	D	E	F
1	832 − 486	+ 486	722 − 509	+ 509	752 − 647	+ 647
2	422 − 281	+ ___	727 − 354	+ ___	928 − 465	+ ___
3	932 − 869	+ ___	432 − 267	+ ___	982 − 345	+ ___
4	972 − 765	+ ___	822 − 590	+ ___	332 − 289	+ ___
5	829 − 59	+ ___	622 − 399	+ ___	522 − 496	+ ___
6	322 − 169	+ ___	922 − 796	+ ___	222 − 95	+ ___

Name _____   Set **10** Worksheet **B**

To find the hidden picture, draw lines from dot to dot. Follow
the order of your answers. Start from the dot with the arrow.

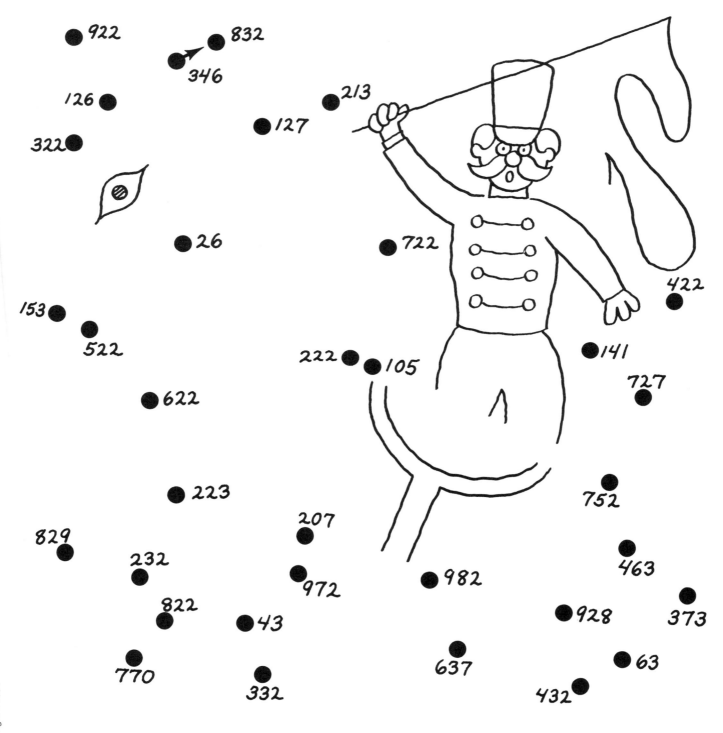

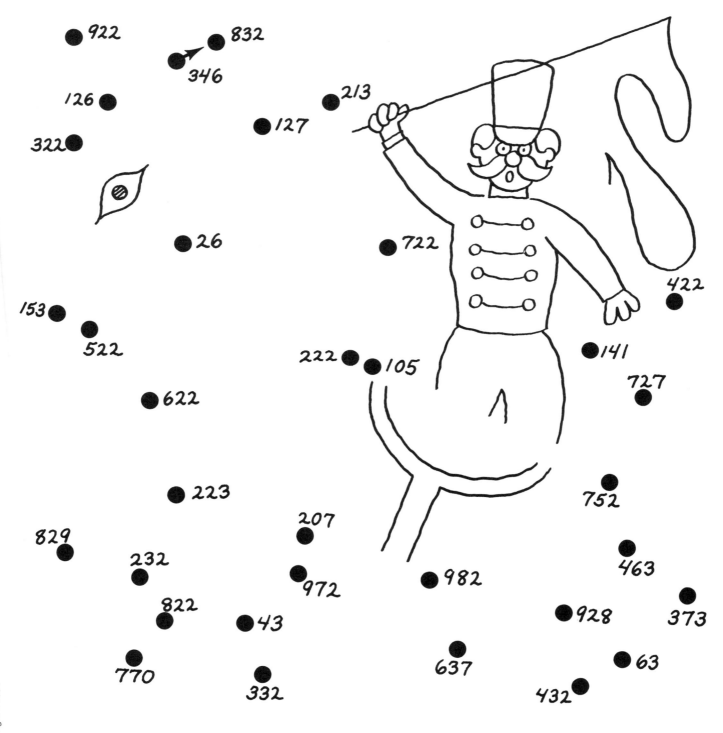

Name _____

Answer each subtraction problem.
Then, check it by addition.

	A	B	C	D	E	F
1	509 − 398	+ 398	927 − 45	+	491 − 173	+
2	790 − 67	+	832 − 524	+	605 − 94	+
3	727 − 485	+	829 − 492	+	914 − 884	+
4	690 − 285	+	808 − 308	+	426 − 134	+
5	481 − 277	+	709 − 635	+	982 − 463	+
6	437 − 325	+	992 − 47	+	729 − 65	+

Name _____

To find the hidden picture, draw lines from dot to dot. Follow
the order of your answers. Start from the dot with the arrow.

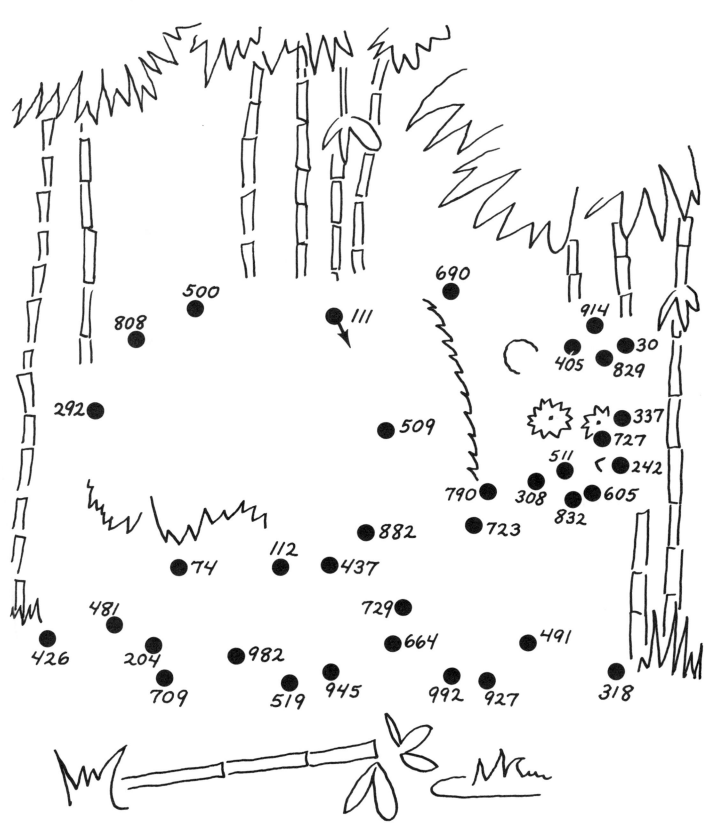

Name _____ Set **12** Worksheet **A**

Answer each subtraction problem.
Then, check it by addition.

	A	B	C	D	E	F
1	763 − 559	+	493 − 87	+	743 − 695	+
2	749 − 537	+	536 − 85	+	643 − 429	+
3	933 − 877	+	893 − 786	+	863 − 156	+
4	843 − 695	+	443 − 55	+	939 − 86	+
5	938 − 878	+	543 − 89	+	243 − 67	+
6	343 − 285	+	943 − 879	+	473 − 236	+

Name _____

To find the hidden picture, draw lines from dot to dot. Follow
the order of your answers. Start from the dot with the arrow.

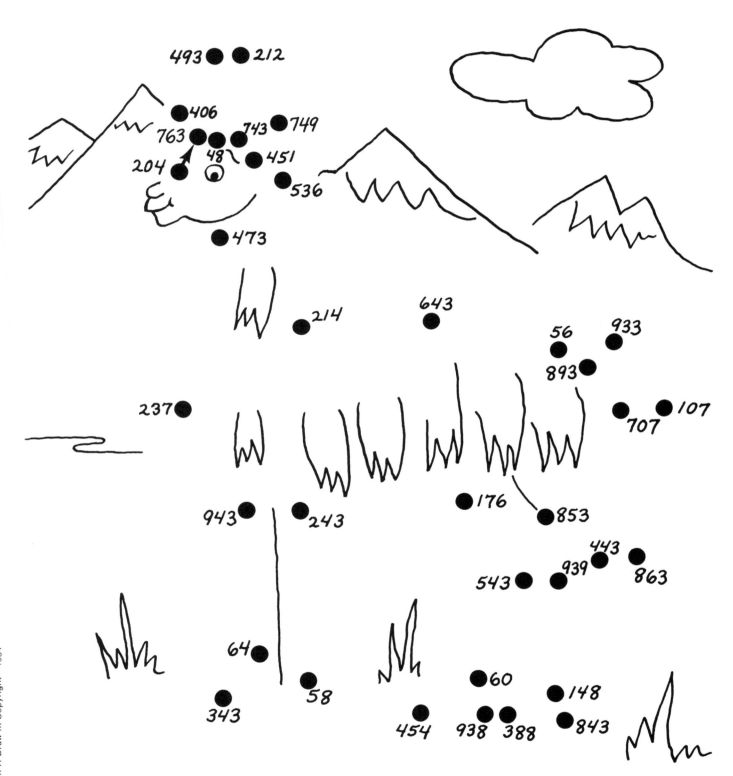

Name _____

Answer each subtraction problem.
Then, check it by addition.

	A	B	C	D	E	F
1	883 − 255	+ ____	833 − 691	+ ____	633 − 334	+ ____
2	723 − 617	+ ____	863 − 745	+ ____	943 − 576	+ ____
3	634 − 522	+ ____	733 − 597	+ ____	623 − 465	+ ____
4	532 − 461	+ ____	843 − 798	+ ____	739 − 695	+ ____
5	613 − 506	+ ____	743 − 676	+ ____	643 − 468	+ ____
6	435 − 392	+ ____	543 − 196	+ ____	233 − 197	+ ____

To find the hidden picture, draw lines from dot to dot. Follow the order of your answers. Start from the dot with the arrow.

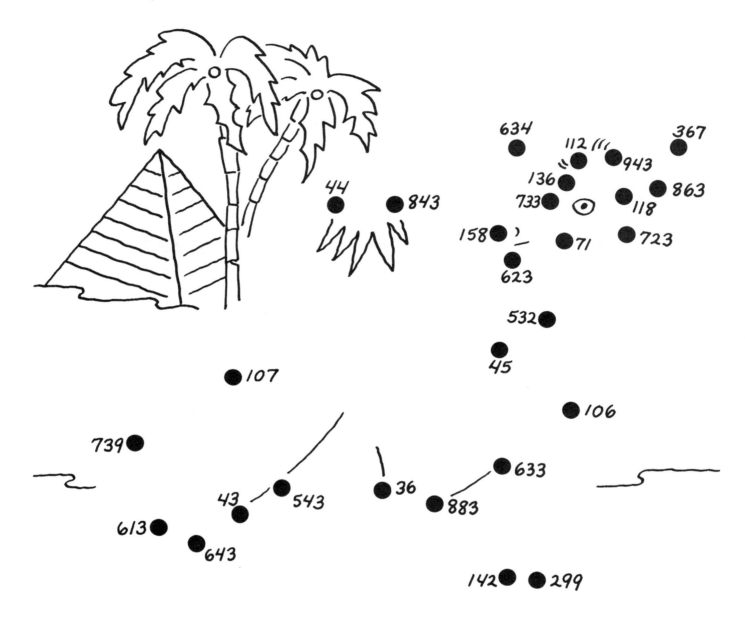

Name _____ Set **14** Worksheet **A**

Answer each subtraction problem.
Then, check it by addition.

	A	B	C	D	E	F

1
$$\begin{array}{r}9,337\\-6,486\\\hline\end{array}\quad +\ \underline{\qquad}\quad \begin{array}{r}9,333\\-8,777\\\hline\end{array}\quad +\ \underline{\qquad}\quad \begin{array}{r}8,432\\-7,695\\\hline\end{array}\quad +\ \underline{\qquad}$$

2
$$\begin{array}{r}8,338\\-5,986\\\hline\end{array}\quad +\ \underline{\qquad}\quad \begin{array}{r}5,233\\-3,459\\\hline\end{array}\quad +\ \underline{\qquad}\quad \begin{array}{r}9,438\\-6,595\\\hline\end{array}\quad +\ \underline{\qquad}$$

3
$$\begin{array}{r}4,339\\-2,895\\\hline\end{array}\quad +\ \underline{\qquad}\quad \begin{array}{r}8,633\\-5,478\\\hline\end{array}\quad +\ \underline{\qquad}\quad \begin{array}{r}6,443\\-5,699\\\hline\end{array}\quad +\ \underline{\qquad}$$

4
$$\begin{array}{r}4,343\\-3,928\\\hline\end{array}\quad +\ \underline{\qquad}\quad \begin{array}{r}3,437\\-2,985\\\hline\end{array}\quad +\ \underline{\qquad}\quad \begin{array}{r}5,832\\-3,729\\\hline\end{array}\quad +\ \underline{\qquad}$$

5
$$\begin{array}{r}6,389\\-5,965\\\hline\end{array}\quad +\ \underline{\qquad}\quad \begin{array}{r}5,329\\-4,698\\\hline\end{array}\quad +\ \underline{\qquad}\quad \begin{array}{r}3,443\\-1,686\\\hline\end{array}\quad +\ \underline{\qquad}$$

Name _____

To find the hidden picture, draw lines from dot to dot. Follow the order of your answers. Start from the dot with the arrow.

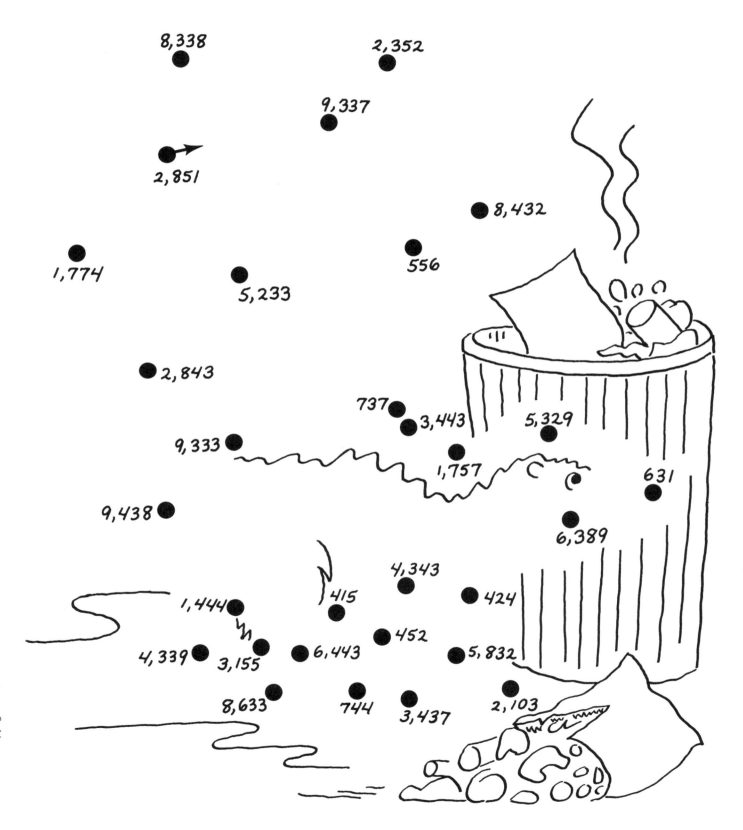

8,338

2,352

9,337

2,851

8,432

1,774

556

5,233

2,843

737

3,443

5,329

9,333

1,757

631

9,438

6,389

4,343

415

424

1,444

452

4,339

3,155

6,443

5,832

8,633

744

3,437

2,103

Name _____

Answer each subtraction problem.
Then, check it by addition.

	A	B	C	D	E	F

1

$\begin{array}{r} 4,093 \\ -2,874 \\ \hline \end{array}$ + _____ $\begin{array}{r} 9,233 \\ -5,678 \\ \hline \end{array}$ + _____ $\begin{array}{r} 8,231 \\ -\ \ \ 597 \\ \hline \end{array}$ + _____

2

$\begin{array}{r} 8,047 \\ -5,843 \\ \hline \end{array}$ + _____ $\begin{array}{r} 6,310 \\ -5,497 \\ \hline \end{array}$ + _____ $\begin{array}{r} 3,143 \\ -2,958 \\ \hline \end{array}$ + _____

3

$\begin{array}{r} 4,038 \\ -3,456 \\ \hline \end{array}$ + _____ $\begin{array}{r} 7,893 \\ -7,682 \\ \hline \end{array}$ + _____ $\begin{array}{r} 8,137 \\ -6,596 \\ \hline \end{array}$ + _____

4

$\begin{array}{r} 5,393 \\ -\ \ \ 428 \\ \hline \end{array}$ + _____ $\begin{array}{r} 9,832 \\ -9,076 \\ \hline \end{array}$ + _____ $\begin{array}{r} 7,940 \\ -5,878 \\ \hline \end{array}$ + _____

5

$\begin{array}{r} 8,295 \\ -4,952 \\ \hline \end{array}$ + _____ $\begin{array}{r} 4,309 \\ -2,893 \\ \hline \end{array}$ + _____ $\begin{array}{r} 6,429 \\ -\ \ \ 752 \\ \hline \end{array}$ + _____

Name _____   Set **15** Worksheet **B**

To find the hidden picture, draw lines from dot to dot. Follow
the order of your answers. Start from the dot with the arrow.

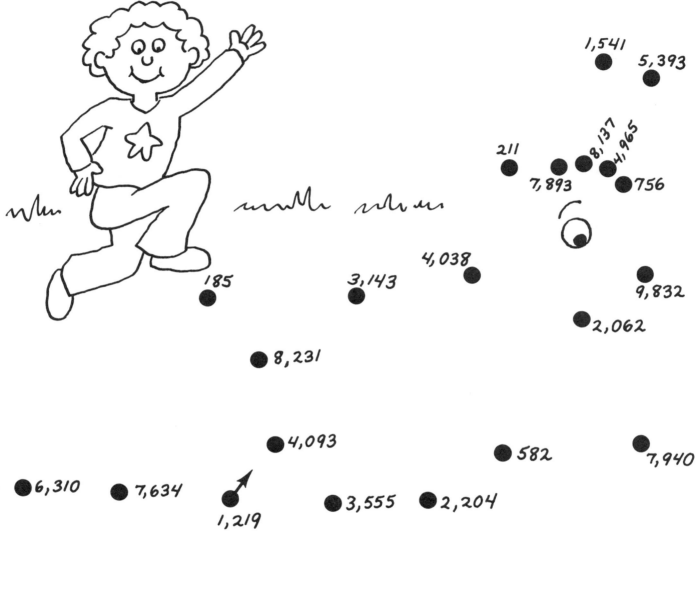

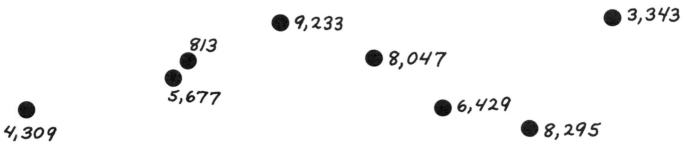

Name _____

Answer each subtraction problem.
Then, check it by addition.

	A	B	C	D	E	F
1	7,436 −5,675	+ _____	9,695 −6,263	+ _____	8,937 −5,843	+ _____
2	4,309 −1,416	+ _____	7,940 −2,062	+ _____	6,310 − 813	+ _____
3	4,093 −1,219	+ _____	9,389 −7,256	+ _____	8,231 −7,634	+ _____
4	9,233 −3,555	+ _____	5,393 − 428	+ _____	3,143 − 175	+ _____
5	8,295 −3,343	+ _____	8,137 −1,541	+ _____	8,047 −2,205	+ _____

Name _____   Set **16** Worksheet **B**

To find the hidden picture, draw lines from dot to dot. Follow the order of your answers. Start from the dot with the arrow.

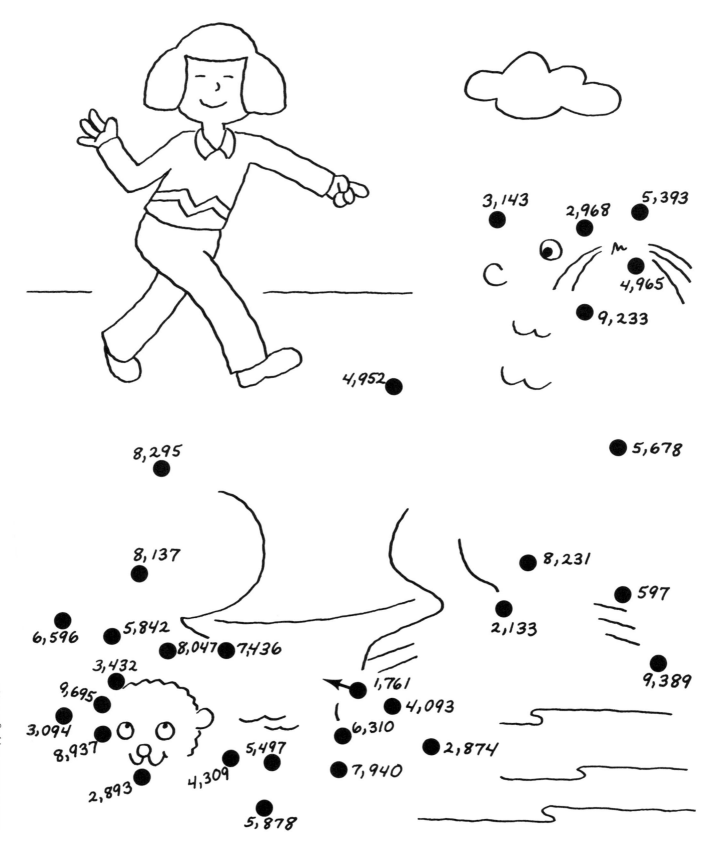

Name _____

Answer each subtraction problem.
Then, check it by addition.

	A	B	C	D	E	F

1
```
   844            894            794
 - 579    +    - 129    +    - 386    +
 _____  ____  _____  ____  _____  ____
```

2
```
   854            654            874
 - 286    +    - 376    +    - 652    +
 _____  ____  _____  ____  _____  ____
```

3
```
   744            847            954
 - 277    +    - 472    +    - 215    +
 _____  ____  _____  ____  _____  ____
```

4
```
   944            764            964
 - 158    +    - 435    +    - 105    +
 _____  ____  _____  ____  _____  ____
```

5
```
   974            940            244
 - 568    +    - 373    +    -  87    +
 _____  ____  _____  ____  _____  ____
```

6
```
   344            544          1,044
 - 167    +    - 249    +    - 327    +
 _____  ____  _____  ____  _____  ____
```

To find the hidden picture, draw lines from dot to dot. Follow
the order of your answers. Start from the dot with the arrow.

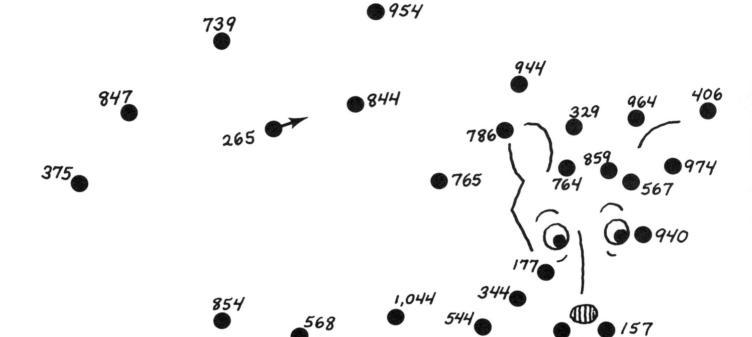

954
739
944
847
844
964
406
265
329
786
859
974
375
765
764
567
940
177
854
344
1,044
568
544
157
654
244
278
408
295
222
894
717

794

744
874

467

Answer each subtraction problem.
Then, check it by addition.

	A	B	C	D	E	F
1	2,749 −1,683	+ ____	8,644 −3,486	+ ____	5,434 −4,329	+ ____
2	1,844 − 765	+ ____	6,948 −3,351	+ ____	4,464 − 715	+ ____
3	7,444 −4,157	+ ____	1,454 − 605	+ ____	8,454 −4,526	+ ____
4	8,444 −5,239	+ ____	5,444 −3,397	+ ____	7,294 −5,086	+ ____
5	7,547 −4,386	+ ____	4,446 − 653	+ ____	4,344 −2,967	+ ____

Name _____

To find the hidden picture, draw lines from dot to dot. Follow the order of your answers. Start from the dot with the arrow.

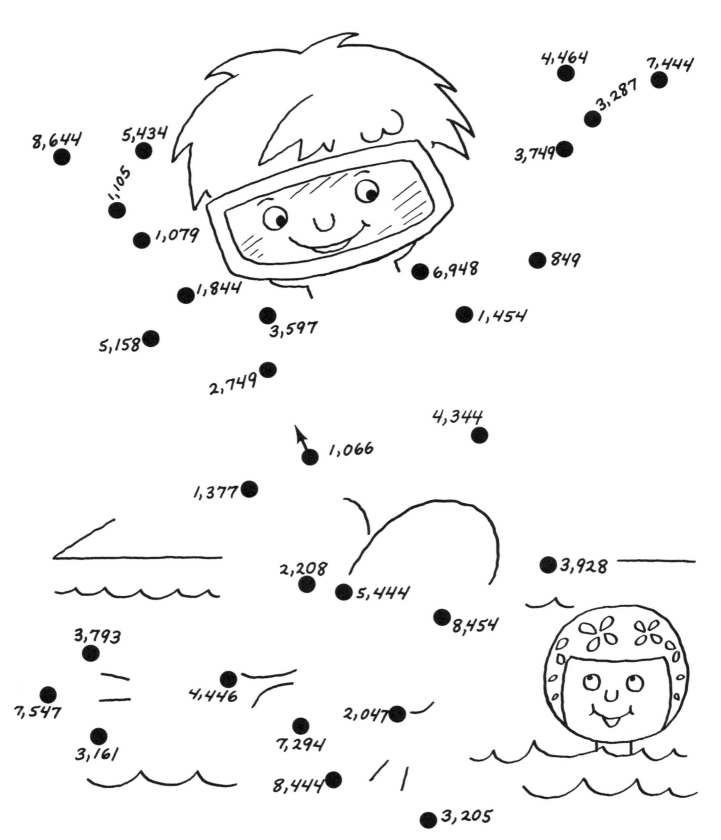

Name _____ Set **19** Worksheet **A**

Answer each subtraction problem.
Then, check it by addition.

	A	B	C	D	E	F

1
$$\begin{array}{r} 8,446 \\ -870 \end{array}$$ $+$ _____ $$\begin{array}{r} 9,444 \\ -667 \end{array}$$ $+$ _____ $$\begin{array}{r} 8,435 \\ -7,924 \end{array}$$ $+$ _____

2
$$\begin{array}{r} 1,844 \\ -277 \end{array}$$ $+$ _____ $$\begin{array}{r} 9,464 \\ -8,958 \end{array}$$ $+$ _____ $$\begin{array}{r} 8,445 \\ -6,873 \end{array}$$ $+$ _____

3
$$\begin{array}{r} 7,444 \\ -6,881 \end{array}$$ $+$ _____ $$\begin{array}{r} 5,648 \\ -5,051 \end{array}$$ $+$ _____ $$\begin{array}{r} 8,644 \\ -2,048 \end{array}$$ $+$ _____

4
$$\begin{array}{r} 3,482 \\ -2,941 \end{array}$$ $+$ _____ $$\begin{array}{r} 6,474 \\ -5,869 \end{array}$$ $+$ _____ $$\begin{array}{r} 8,849 \\ -253 \end{array}$$ $+$ _____

5
$$\begin{array}{r} 8,434 \\ -7,986 \end{array}$$ $+$ _____ $$\begin{array}{r} 6,?49 \\ -4,567 \end{array}$$ $+$ _____ $$\begin{array}{r} 7,344 \\ -5,397 \end{array}$$ $+$ _____

To find the hidden picture, draw lines from dot to dot. Follow
the order of your answers. Start from the dot with the arrow.

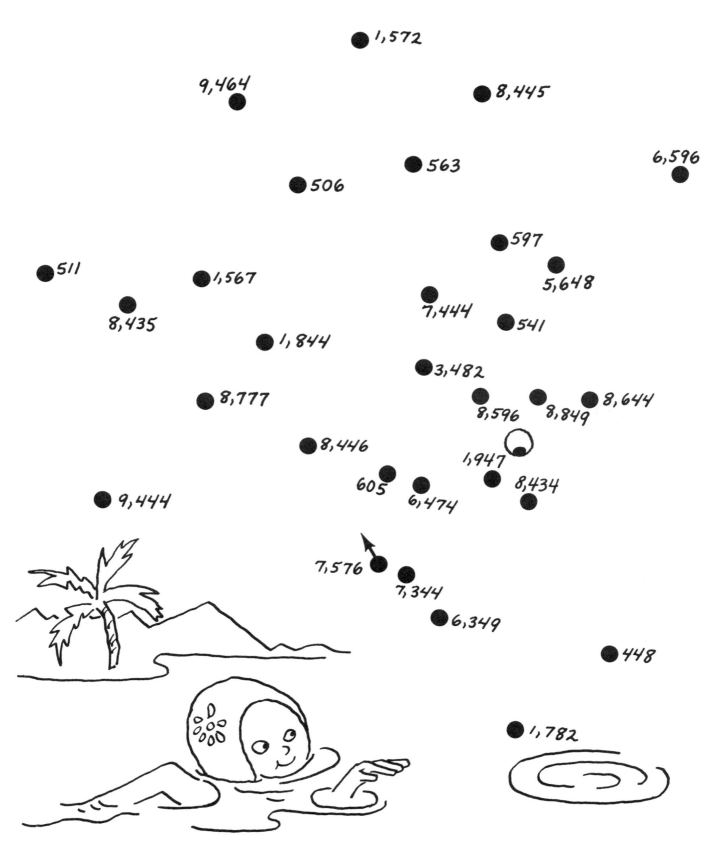

Name _____

Answer each subtraction problem.
Then, check it by addition.

	A	B	C	D	E	F
1	6,043 −5,829	+ ___	9,143 −8,267	+ ___	4,213 −3,238	+ ___
2	4,090 − 87	+ ___	8,210 −5,736	+ ___	5,314 −2,529	+ ___
3	5,210 −4,313	+ ___	8,072 −7,119	+ ___	3,240 −2,786	+ ___
4	4,320 −2,753	+ ___	4,824 −3,713	+ ___	7,109 −6,620	+ ___
5	8,764 −5,216	+ ___	7,442 −7,434	+ ___	2,143 −1,248	+ ___

To find the hidden picture, draw lines from dot to dot. Follow the order of your answers. Start from the dot with the arrow.

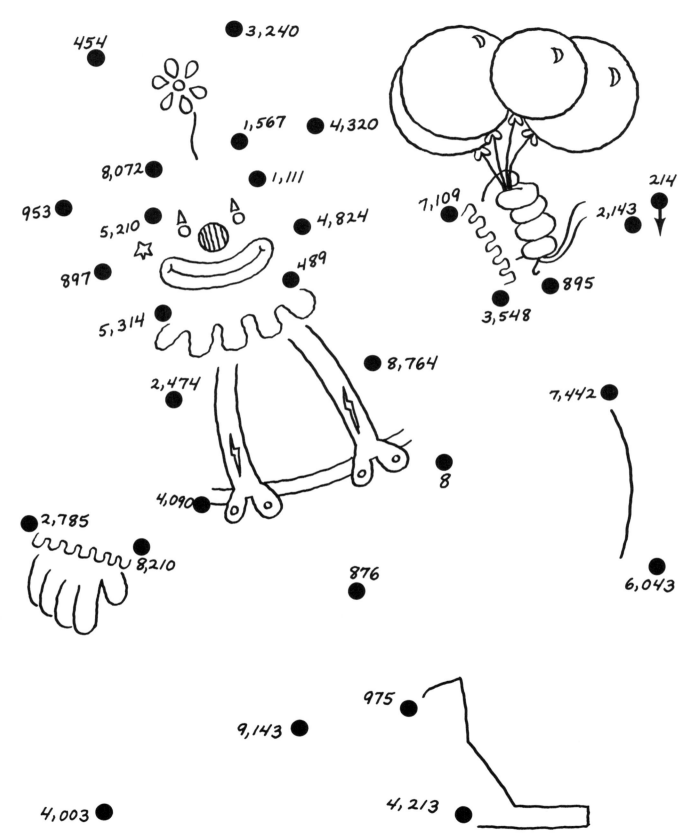

454

3,240

1,567   4,320

8,072

1,111

953

5,210

4,824

897

489

5,314

2,474

8,764

4,090

2,785

8,210

876

7,109

2,143

214

895

3,548

7,442

8

6,043

975

9,143

4,003

4,213

Name _____

Answer each subtraction problem.
Then, check it by addition.

	A	B	C	D	E	F

1

A	B	C	D	E	F
985 − 888	+ _____	8,765 −7,789	+ _____	7,565 −6,897	+ _____

2

| 5,657
 −   89 | + _____ | 9,657
 −8,761 | + _____ | 9,755
 −8,881 | + _____ |

3

| 4,568
 − 590 | + _____ | 4,756
 −3,878 | + _____ | 2,876
 −1,889 | + _____ |

4

| 6,857
 −5,889 | + _____ | 4,576
 −3,898 | + _____ | 5,678
 −4,679 | + _____ |

5

| 8,677
 −7,779 | + _____ | 9,576
 −8,717 | + _____ | 9,856
 −8,883 | + _____ |

To find the hidden picture, draw lines from dot to dot. Follow
the order of your answers. Start from the dot with the arrow.

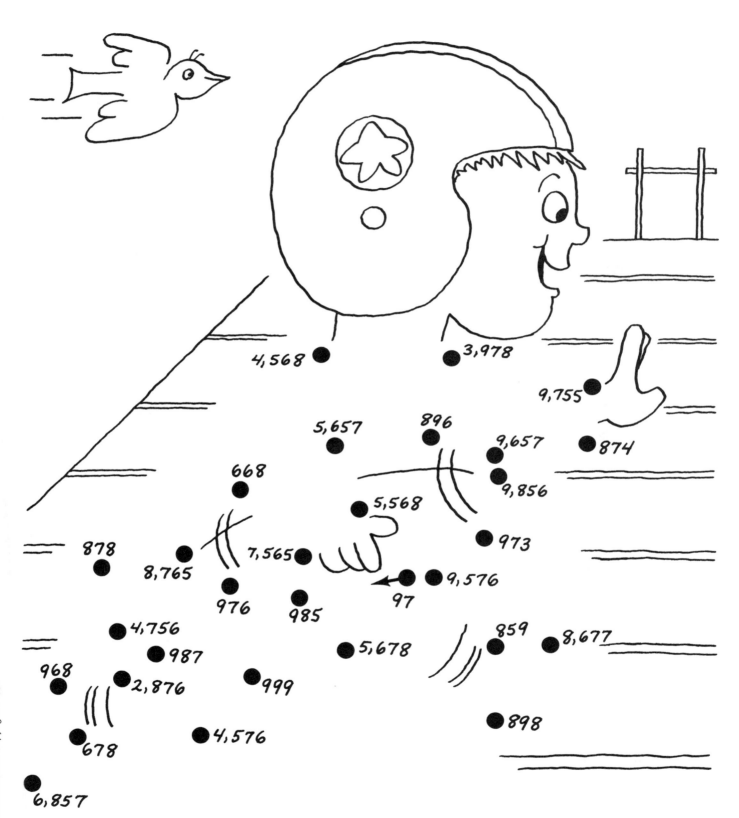

Name _____

Answer each subtraction problem.
Then, check it by addition.

	A	B	C	D	E	F

1.
$$\begin{array}{r} 3,786 \\ -799 \\ \hline \end{array} +$$
$$\begin{array}{r} 8,657 \\ -5,109 \\ \hline \end{array} +$$
$$\begin{array}{r} 8,950 \\ -7,962 \\ \hline \end{array} +$$

2.
$$\begin{array}{r} 4,876 \\ -889 \\ \hline \end{array} +$$
$$\begin{array}{r} 4,756 \\ -3,977 \\ \hline \end{array} +$$
$$\begin{array}{r} 8,325 \\ -7,957 \\ \hline \end{array} +$$

3.
$$\begin{array}{r} 5,785 \\ -3,996 \\ \hline \end{array} +$$
$$\begin{array}{r} 8,758 \\ -7,969 \\ \hline \end{array} +$$
$$\begin{array}{r} 8,567 \\ -2,989 \\ \hline \end{array} +$$

4.
$$\begin{array}{r} 5,786 \\ -4,983 \\ \hline \end{array} +$$
$$\begin{array}{r} 4,856 \\ -3,897 \\ \hline \end{array} +$$
$$\begin{array}{r} 5,765 \\ -698 \\ \hline \end{array} +$$

5.
$$\begin{array}{r} 9,876 \\ -3,899 \\ \hline \end{array} +$$
$$\begin{array}{r} 8,656 \\ -3,688 \\ \hline \end{array} +$$
$$\begin{array}{r} 9,768 \\ -99 \\ \hline \end{array} +$$

Name _____   Set **22** Worksheet **B**

To find the hidden picture, draw lines from dot to dot. Follow
the order of your answers. Start from the dot with the arrow.

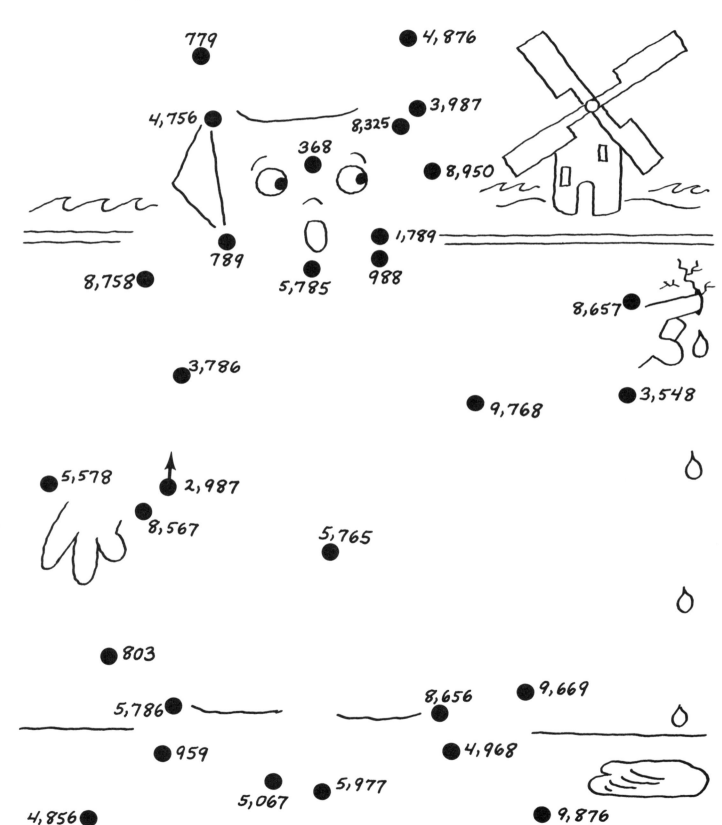

779

4,876

4,756   8,325   3,987

368

8,950

789   1,789

8,758   5,785   988

8,657

3,786

3,548

9,768

5,578   2,987

8,567   5,765

803

8,656   9,669

5,786   4,968

959

5,067   5,977   9,876

4,856

Name _____

Answer each subtraction problem.
Then, check it by addition.

	A	B	C	D	E	F

1
$$905 - 68 \qquad +$$
$$901 - 468 \qquad +$$
$$506 - 497 \qquad +$$

2
$$505 - 308 \qquad +$$
$$807 - 259 \qquad +$$
$$409 - 33 \qquad +$$

3
$$902 - 365 \qquad +$$
$$605 - 259 \qquad +$$
$$906 - 549 \qquad +$$

4
$$808 - 209 \qquad +$$
$$401 - 184 \qquad +$$
$$803 - 179 \qquad +$$

5
$$809 - 44 \qquad +$$
$$870 - 595 \qquad +$$
$$708 - 437 \qquad +$$

6
$$904 - 848 \qquad +$$
$$606 - 478 \qquad +$$
$$604 - 178 \qquad +$$

Name _____   Set **23** Worksheet **B**

To find the hidden picture, draw lines from dot to dot. Follow
the order of your answers. Start from the dot with the arrow.

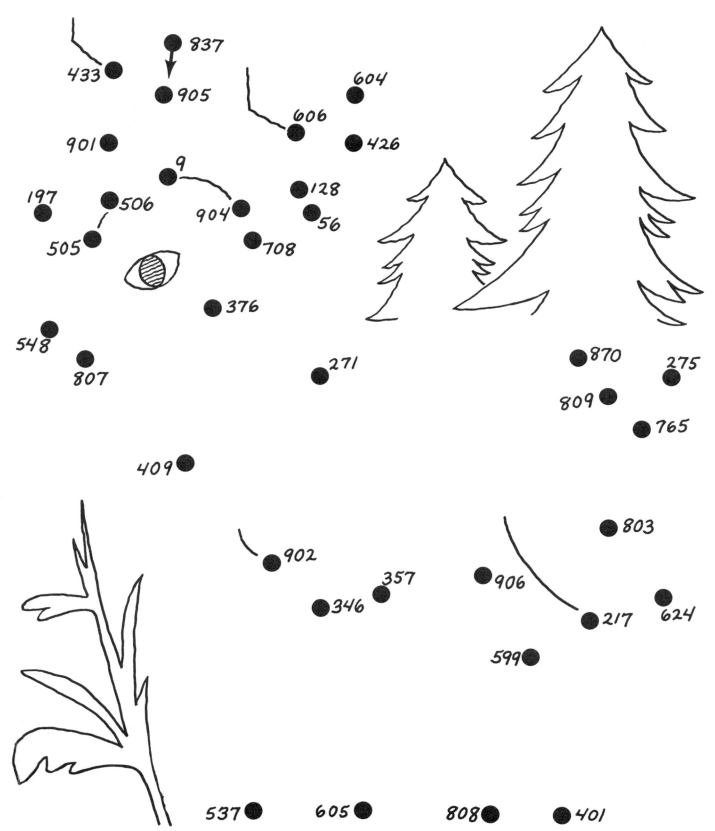

Name _____   Set **24**   Worksheet **A**

Answer each subtraction problem.
Then, check it by addition.

	A	B	C	D	E	F

1
```
   900          807          700
 - 180    +   -  39    +   - 505    +
 ─────  ─────  ─────  ─────  ─────  ─────
```

2
```
   902          800          904
 - 870    +   - 386    +   - 876    +
 ─────  ─────  ─────  ─────  ─────  ─────
```

3
```
   820          706          100
 - 568    +   - 498    +   -  79    +
 ─────  ─────  ─────  ─────  ─────  ─────
```

4
```
   200          300          307
 - 176    +   - 290    +   - 289    +
 ─────  ─────  ─────  ─────  ─────  ─────
```

5
```
   605          560          400
 - 387    +   - 493    +   - 374    +
 ─────  ─────  ─────  ─────  ─────  ─────
```

6
```
   500          600          709
 - 429    +   - 350    +   - 305    +
 ─────  ─────  ─────  ─────  ─────  ─────
```

Math-A-Draw III Copyright © 1984

Name _____

To find the hidden picture, draw lines from dot to dot. Follow
the order of your answers. Start from the dot with the arrow.

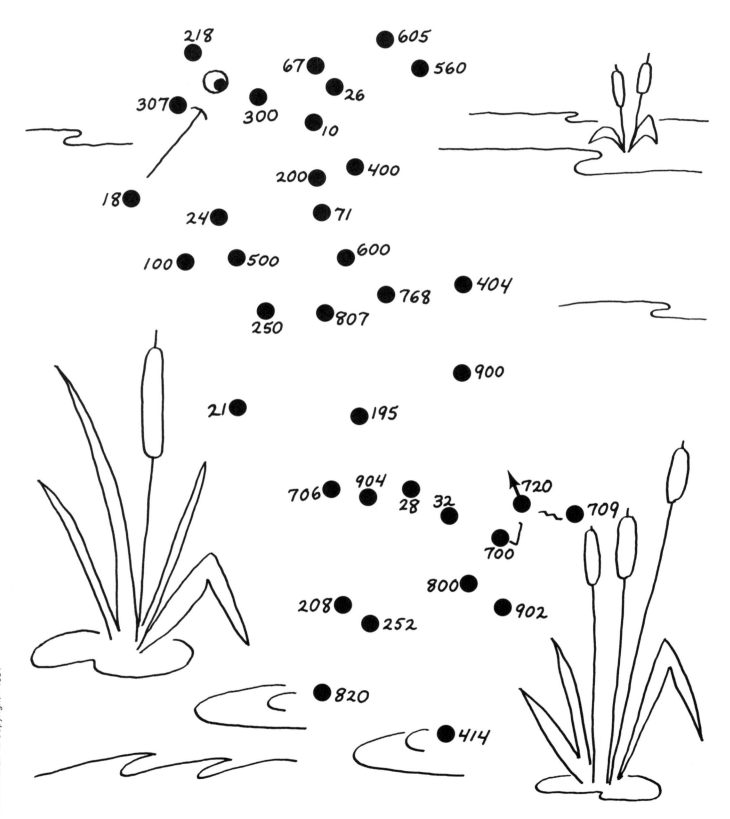

Name _____

Answer each subtraction problem.
Then, check it by addition.

	A	B	C	D	E	F
1	300 − 248	+ ___	409 − 368	+ ___	400 − 370	+ ___
2	480 − 376	+ ___	100 − 82	+ ___	500 − 397	+ ___
3	602 − 397	+ ___	600 − 503	+ ___	704 − 685	+ ___
4	700 − 472	+ ___	405 − 278	+ ___	397 − 246	+ ___
5	508 − 369	+ ___	800 − 659	+ ___	607 − 384	+ ___
6	200 − 190	+ ___	301 − 179	+ ___	900 − 846	+ ___

To find the hidden picture, draw lines from dot to dot. Follow the order of your answers. Start from the dot with the arrow.

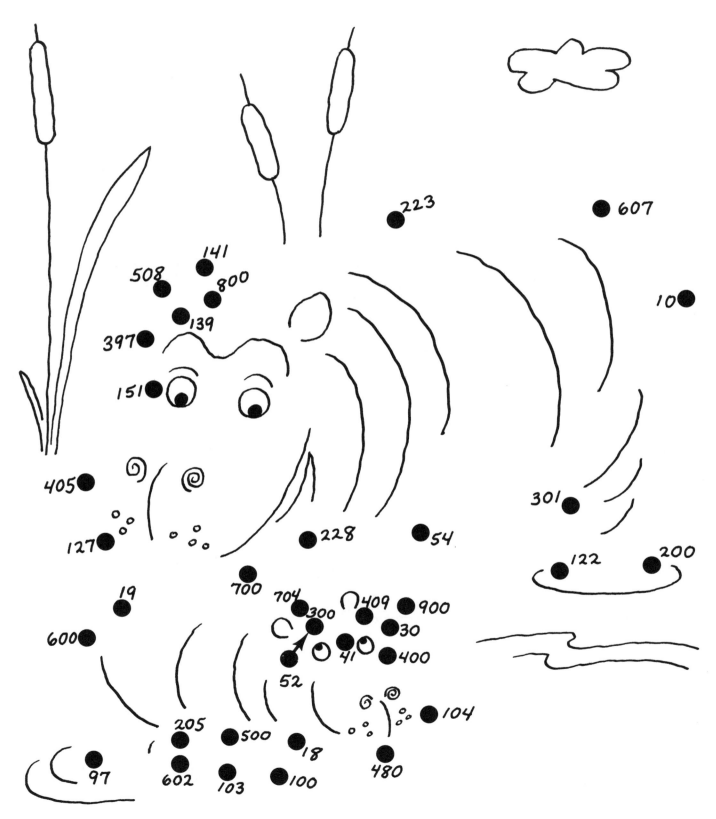

Name _____

Answer each subtraction problem.
Then, check it by addition.

	A	B	C	D	E	F
1	1,000 − 547	+ _____	1,010 − 375	+ _____	9,000 − 972	+ _____
2	1,502 − 876	+ _____	2,000 − 825	+ _____	3,406 −2,943	+ _____
3	8,000 − 476	+ _____	2,100 − 396	+ _____	3,000 −1,532	+ _____
4	4,000 − 689	+ _____	3,080 − 476	+ _____	5,000 − 468	+ _____
5	7,065 −3,892	+ _____	6,000 −3,358	+ _____	7,000 −6,402	+ _____

Math-A-Draw III Copyright © 1984

Name _____

To find the hidden picture, draw lines from dot to dot. Follow the order of your answers. Start from the dot with the arrow.

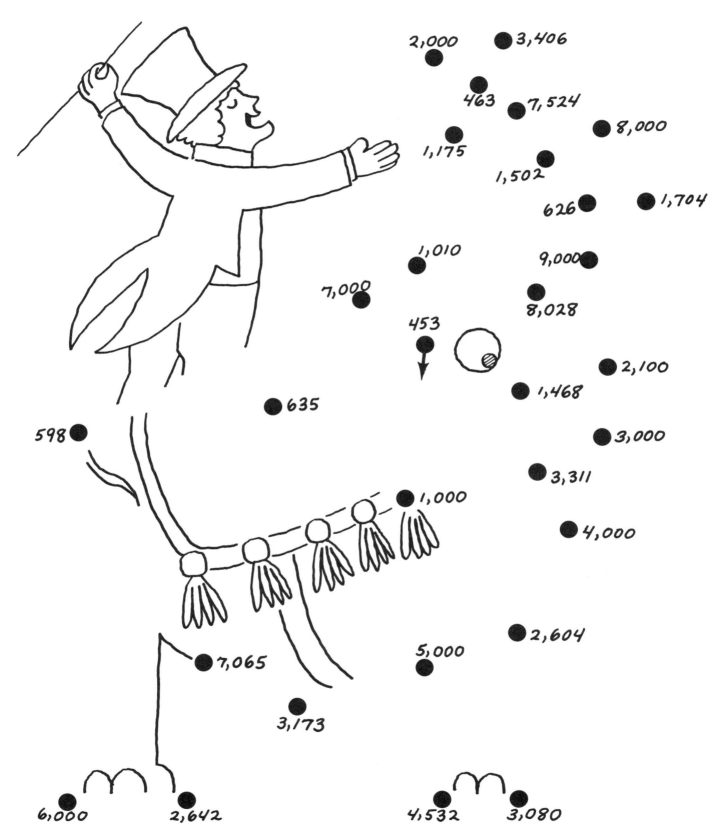

Answer each subtraction problem.
Then, check it by addition.

	A	B	C	D	E	F

1
```
  9,086          5,010          5,000
 -4,847   +    -3,879   +    -4,276   +
 _____  ___   _____  ___   _____  ___
```

2
```
  7,109          9,576          4,800
 -  489   +    -8,751   +    -  976   +
 _____  ___   _____  ___   _____  ___
```

3
```
  9,074          8,005          9,568
 -3,727   +    -5,789   +    -1,599   +
 _____  ___   _____  ___   _____  ___
```

4
```
  7,080          8,675          6,000
 -3,999   +    -  988   +    -3,850   +
 _____  ___   _____  ___   _____  ___
```

5
```
  8,567          8,000          9,089
 -7,699   +    -6,500   +    -5,900   +
 _____  ___   _____  ___   _____  ___
```

To find the hidden picture, draw lines from dot to dot. Follow the order of your answers. Start from the dot with the arrow.

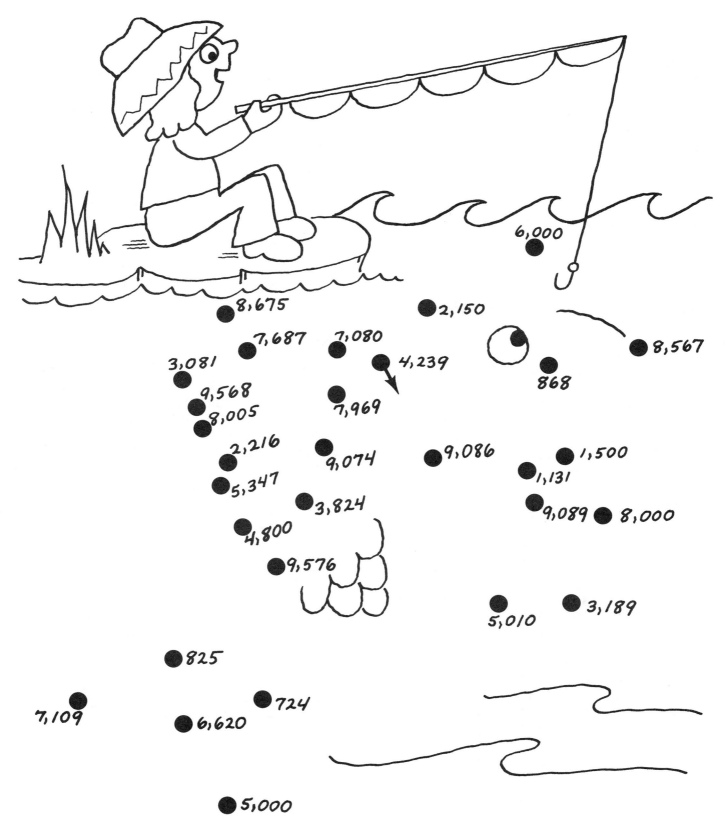

Answer Key

Set 1

	A	B	C	D	E	F
1.	66	70	8	20	11	40
2.	21	60	12	30	37	80
3.	17	50	1	90	3	10
4.	315	350	208	270	103	190
5.	241	250	322	380	217	260
6.	110	150	246	450	263	390

Set 2

	A	B	C	D	E	F
1.	107	180	203	780	312	580
2.	220	450	112	770	307	320
3.	622	690	954	990	420	840
4.	301	640	223	670	317	340
5.	115	160	510	930	153	480
6.	127	350	702	720	124	390

Set 3

	A	B	C	D	E	F
1.	220	300	10	800	441	806
2.	105	920	200	720	601	660
3.	53	808	613	640	131	509
4.	244	707	585	807	333	409
5.	206	530	114	307	141	490
6.	616	709	514	540	740	990

Set 4

	A	B	C	D	E	F
1.	48	51	75	81	1	61
2.	5	71	35	91	10	31
3.	25	41	206	221	151	181
4.	626	691	383	391	547	571
5.	316	341	306	321	106	191
6.	677	681	311	351	745	781

Set 5

	A	B	C	D	E	F
1.	942	991	728	761	137	971
2.	615	941	206	361	416	751
3.	16	821	908	961	329	861
4.	316	871	847	851	215	571
5.	221	651	426	891	733	741
6.	129	841	625	946	6	771

Set 6

	A	B	C	D	E	F
1.	732	814	593	915	103	121
2.	512	951	551	919	393	816
3.	853	881	821	918	24	431
4.	80	413	614	841	403	941
5.	860	917	715	791	236	491
6.	422	751	423	831	371	615

Set 7

	A	B	C	D	E	F
1.	550	813	304	410	326	819
2.	264	708	103	690	372	408
3.	309	911	273	806	111	891
4.	834	905	256	580	110	913
5.	114	341	414	431	721	816
6.	623	709	354	999	622	718

Set 8

	A	B	C	D	E	F
1.	35	42	23	32	313	342
2.	643	725	731	821	642	723
3.	433	462	803	832	307	322
4.	512	522	535	629	724	742
5.	72	128	491	526	334	425
6.	635	982	182	529	81	329

Set 9

	A	B	C	D	E	F
1.	117	922	54	429	123	852
2.	216	782	142	526	311	827
3.	61	629	282	927	132	726
4.	71	829	116	322	712	722
5.	531	622	313	822	332	427
6.	261	821	284	326	32	825

Set 10

	A	B	C	D	E	F
1.	346	832	213	722	105	752
2.	141	422	373	727	463	928
3.	63	932	165	432	637	982
4.	207	972	232	822	43	332
5.	770	829	223	622	26	522
6.	153	322	126	922	127	222

Set 11

	A	B	C	D	E	F
1.	111	509	882	927	318	491
2.	723	790	308	832	511	605
3.	242	727	337	829	30	914
4.	405	690	500	808	292	426
5.	204	481	74	709	519	982
6.	112	437	945	992	664	729

Set 12

	A	B	C	D	E	F
1.	204	763	406	493	48	743
2.	212	749	451	536	214	643
3.	56	933	107	893	707	863
4.	148	843	388	443	853	939
5.	60	938	454	543	176	243
6.	58	343	64	943	237	473

Set 13

	A	B	C	D	E	F
1.	628	883	142	833	299	633
2.	106	723	118	863	367	943
3.	112	634	136	733	158	623
4.	71	532	45	843	44	739
5.	107	613	67	743	175	643
6.	43	435	347	543	36	233

Set 14

	A	B	C	D	E	F
1.	2,851	9,337	556	9,333	737	8,432
2.	2,352	8,338	1,774	5,233	2,843	9,438
3.	1,444	4,339	3,155	8,633	744	6,443
4.	415	4,343	452	3,437	2,103	5,832
5.	424	6,389	631	5,329	1,757	3,443

Set 15

	A	B	C	D	E	F
1.	1,219	4,093	3,555	9,233	7,634	8,231
2.	2,204	8,047	813	6,310	185	3,143
3.	582	4,038	211	7,893	1,541	8,137
4.	4,965	5,393	756	9,832	2,062	7,940
5.	3,343	8,295	1,416	4,309	5,677	6,429

Set 16

	A	B	C	D	E	F
1.	1,761	7,436	3,432	9,695	3,094	8,937
2.	2,893	4,309	5,878	7,940	5,497	6,310
3.	2,874	4,093	2,133	9,389	597	8,231
4.	5,678	9,233	4,965	5,393	2,968	3,143
5.	4,952	8,295	6,596	8,137	5,842	8,047

Set 17

	A	B	C	D	E	F
1.	265	844	765	894	408	794
2.	568	854	278	654	222	874
3.	467	744	375	847	739	954
4.	786	944	329	764	859	964
5.	406	974	567	940	157	244
6.	177	344	295	544	717	1,044

Set 18

	A	B	C	D	E	F
1.	1,066	2,749	5,158	8,644	1,105	5,434
2.	1,079	1,844	3,597	6,948	3,749	4,464
3.	3,287	7,444	849	1,454	3,928	8,454
4.	3,205	8,444	2,047	5,444	2,208	7,294
5.	3,161	7,547	3,793	4,446	1,377	4,344

Set 19

	A	B	C	D	E	F
1.	7,576	8,446	8,777	9,444	511	8,435
2.	1,567	1,844	506	9,464	1,572	8,445
3.	563	7,444	597	5,648	6,596	8,644
4.	541	3,482	605	6,474	8,596	8,849
5.	448	8,434	1,782	6,349	1,947	7,344

Set 20

	A	B	C	D	E	F
1.	214	6,043	876	9,143	975	4,213
2.	4,003	4,090	2,474	8,210	2,785	5,314
3.	897	5,210	953	8,072	454	3,240
4.	1,567	4,320	1,111	4,824	489	7,109
5.	3,548	8,764	8	7,442	895	2,143

Set 21

	A	B	C	D	E	F
1.	97	985	976	8,765	668	7,565
2.	5,568	5,657	896	9,657	874	9,755
3.	3,978	4,568	878	4,756	987	2,876
4.	968	6,857	678	4,576	999	5,678
5.	898	8,677	859	9,576	973	9,856

Set 22

	A	B	C	D	E	F
1.	2,987	3,786	3,548	8,657	988	8,950
2.	3,987	4,876	779	4,756	368	8,325
3.	1,789	5,785	789	8,758	5,578	8,567
4.	803	5,786	959	4,856	5,067	5,765
5.	5,977	9,876	4,968	8,656	9,669	9,768

Set 23

	A	B	C	D	E	F
1.	837	905	433	901	9	506
2.	197	505	548	807	376	409
3.	537	902	346	605	357	906
4.	599	808	217	401	624	803
5.	765	809	275	870	271	708
6.	56	904	128	606	426	604

Set 24

	A	B	C	D	E	F
1.	720	900	768	807	195	700
2.	32	902	414	800	28	904
3.	252	820	208	706	21	100
4.	24	200	10	300	18	307
5.	218	605	67	560	26	400
6.	71	500	250	600	404	709

Set 25

	A	B	C	D	E	F
1.	52	300	41	409	30	400
2.	104	480	18	100	103	500
3.	205	602	97	600	19	704
4.	228	700	127	405	151	397
5.	139	508	141	800	223	607
6.	10	200	122	301	54	900

Set 26

	A	B	C	D	E	F
1.	453	1,000	635	1,010	8,028	9,000
2.	626	1,502	1,175	2,000	463	3,406
3.	7,524	8,000	1,704	2,100	1,468	3,000
4.	3,311	4,000	2,604	3,080	4,532	5,000
5.	3,173	7,065	2,642	6,000	598	7,000

Set 27

	A	B	C	D	E	F
1.	4,239	9,086	1,131	5,010	724	5,000
2.	6,620	7,109	825	9,576	3,824	4,800
3.	5,347	9,074	2,216	8,005	7,969	9,568
4.	3,081	7,080	7,687	8,675	2,150	6,000
5.	868	8,567	1,500	8,000	3,189	9,089